D1489464

MINCE PIE
and
MISTLETOE

by
PHYLLIS McGINLEY

pictures by
HAROLD BERSON

J. B. LIPPINCOTT COMPANY
Philadelphia   New York

MINCE PIE
and
MISTLETOE

It's Christmas,
It's Christmas,
    Across the world and back,
In Sweden and the Argentine,
    In Ireland and Iraq;
It's Christmas on peninsulas
    And continents and straits,
But chiefly it is Christmas
    In these United States.
Three hundred fifty years and more,
    North, south, and west and east,
Since first our settlers stepped ashore,
    We've kept the gracious Feast
(Except when merriment was banned
    And yuletides grew sedater
On Massachusetts' sober strand.
    I'll tell the story later.)

We hadn't always Santa Claus
    Or garlands in the hall,
But grave or gay,
We kept the Day—
    For children, most of all.

VIRGINIA

Over the sea
From England's isles,
Virginians brought
Their Christmas styles,
Of punch bowl,
Yule log,
Candle glow,
And holly and ivy
And mistletoe.

To every manor house
By the dozens
Came aunts and uncles
And kissing-cousins,
To greet each other with love and laughter
And sit to the feast that followed after.
How the tables groaned!

How the air was murky
With odors of sausage
And duck and turkey,
Of hams
And yams
Where the sweet sauce trickled,
Of jellies and jams
And walnuts, pickled.
It must have been fine
(In a child's opinion)
To celebrate so
In the Old Dominion—
To share the toasts
That were lifted up,
The flaming pudding,
The syllabub cup,
Then to sing old carols and tell old riddles,
And dance the reel to the sound of fiddles.

NEW ENGLAND

The Pilgrims were pious,
The Pilgrims were brave,
They had lands to conquer,
And souls to save.
They were busy and bold
    And worthy, very.
But they didn't hold
    With making merry.
Though they loved the Lord,
Historians say
They never rejoiced
On Christmas Day.

For twenty-two years
From Plymouth's founding
They kept the carols
From ever sounding.
Their lights didn't shine,
Their bells didn't jingle.
They shut their chimneys
On good Kris Kringle,
And termed it pagan,
And thought it shocking
To hang a wreath
Or a Christmas stocking.

No cakes, no presents,
No Christmas mirth,
No "Alleluia!"
No "Peace on earth,"
Nothing but sermons
At Sunday meeting,
And a stern rebuke
For Christmas greeting.
Oh, aren't you glad
That you weren't alive
In sixteen-twenty
Or twenty-five?

THE SOUTHWEST

Yet even before the Pilgrims
    Had trod New England's snow,
They kept in California
    And old New Mexico
The pretty Spanish customs
    Of Christmas long ago.

If you were young in that far-off day,
You took your part in a miracle play.
Dressed in the cloak
That shepherds wear,
You joined your friends
In the village square,
Then trudged through town
With the rest of them,
Seeking the Babe of Bethlehem.

You rapped at each door.
You asked each stranger,
"Where is the Christ Child?
Where is the Manger?"
Till host or his hostess
Took you in.
Ah, then did the festival time begin!
With games and presents
And sweetmeats piled
In earthenware jars,
For every child.

NEW AMSTERDAM

Hooray for the Dutch!
We owe them much,
    Jolly Mynheer and matron—
When they left the sands
Of their Netherlands,
    Saint Nicholas was their patron
(And good Saint Nick,
The children's prince,
Has been our Santa Claus
Ever since.)

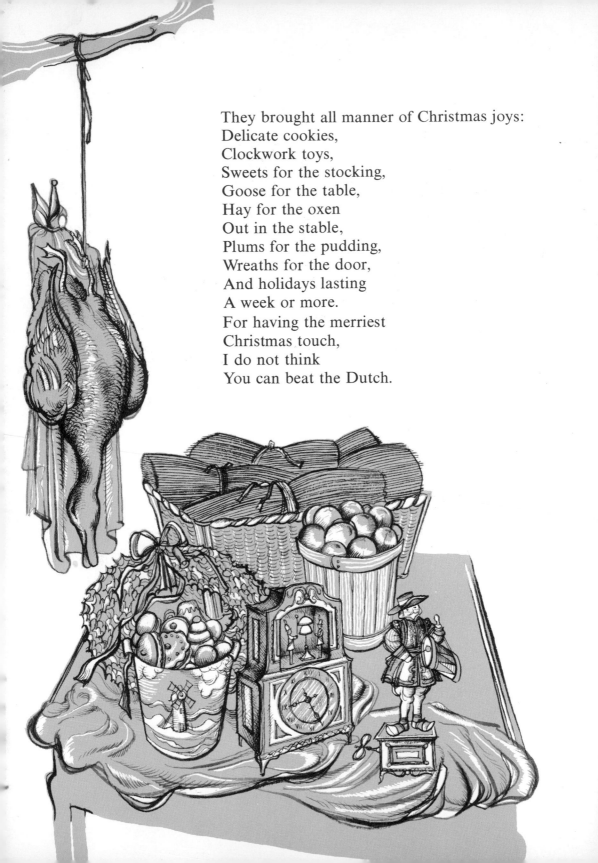

They brought all manner of Christmas joys:
Delicate cookies,
Clockwork toys,
Sweets for the stocking,
Goose for the table,
Hay for the oxen
Out in the stable,
Plums for the pudding,
Wreaths for the door,
And holidays lasting
A week or more.
For having the merriest
Christmas touch,
I do not think
You can beat the Dutch.

LOUISIANA

In old New Orleans,
    Something nice
Happened to children—
    They got gifts twice:
Once when the new year
Sang its warning,
But first on the holy
Christmas morning.
(For that was a French town,
You'll remember,
Where the Creole customs
Ruled December.)

To tall white houses
      Where the breeze
Fluttered the vines
      On balconies,
Relatives came
In a family throng.
There were balls and banquets
The whole week long,
Such Creole food
As you wouldn't believe,
And midnight mass
On Nativity Eve
With the organ playing,
The great bells pealing,
And always a crèche,
With the shepherds, kneeling.

Then "Papa Noel,"
When the hymns were sung,
Showered his presents
On old and young.

THE WESTERN COUNTRY

In many a bleak log cabin,
    On many a rough frontier,
Christmas was plain and scanty
    In the winter of the year.
Yet every childish heart beat high
    As the twenty-fifth drew near.

For the neighbors came in wagons
    From half a state away.
And the old men brought the banjos
    They'd near forgot to play,
While the young folk danced a dos-a-dos
    And clapped for Christmas Day.

There were wooden dolls and rifles
    Carved for a child's surprise.
There was venison in the oven,
    There were piping-hot mince pies,
And maybe a ribboned wreath or two
    To please the little one's eyes.

Though the blizzard roamed
Through the Western air,
Christmas was Christmas
Even there.

THE VICTORIAN YEARS

Victorians loved the Christmas pine.
      Victorians had a mania
For the holiday tree
From Germany
      (By way of Pennsylvania).
They hung its branches
With popcorn chains,
Cranberries, tinsel,
Candy canes,
And lit it with tapers,
Waxy-scented.
(Electric lights
Hadn't been invented.)

Under its boughs
Sat the painted toys
Designed for Victorian
Girls and boys:
The magic lanterns,
The skates and sleds,
The sawdust dolls
With their china heads,
The hoops for rolling
In city parks,
And the balls and beanbags
And Noah's arks.
It's possible *you*
Might prefer to get
Trains,
Or a color-camera set.
But children's wishes
Were less adventury
Back in the peaceful
Nineteenth Century.
So, happy with everything
They saw,
They dropped a curtsy,
Or kissed Papa
Then after a jaunt
On their rocking horses
Sat down to a dinner
Of seven courses.

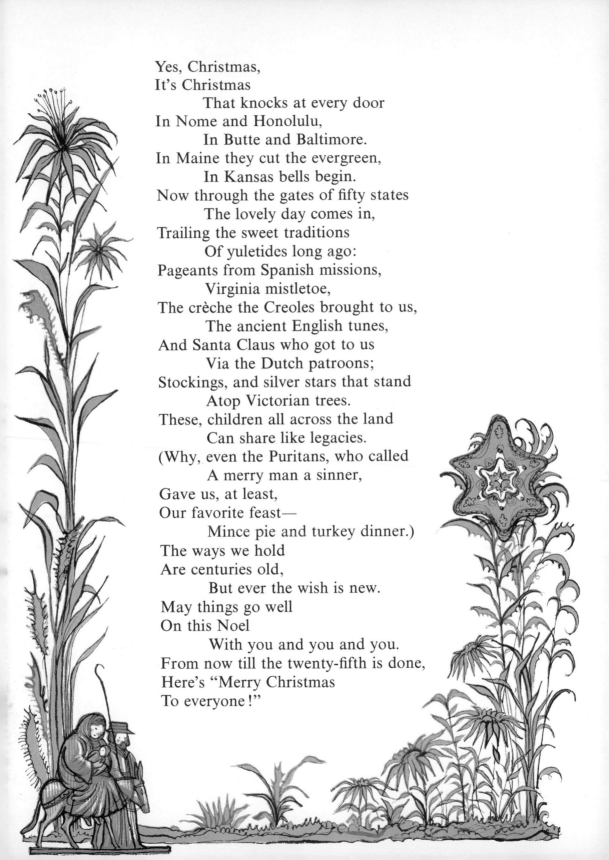

Yes, Christmas,
It's Christmas
  That knocks at every door
In Nome and Honolulu,
  In Butte and Baltimore.
In Maine they cut the evergreen,
  In Kansas bells begin.
Now through the gates of fifty states
  The lovely day comes in,
Trailing the sweet traditions
  Of yuletides long ago:
Pageants from Spanish missions,
  Virginia mistletoe,
The crèche the Creoles brought to us,
  The ancient English tunes,
And Santa Claus who got to us
  Via the Dutch patroons;
Stockings, and silver stars that stand
  Atop Victorian trees.
These, children all across the land
  Can share like legacies.
(Why, even the Puritans, who called
  A merry man a sinner,
Gave us, at least,
Our favorite feast—
  Mince pie and turkey dinner.)
The ways we hold
Are centuries old,
  But ever the wish is new.
May things go well
On this Noel
  With you and you and you.
From now till the twenty-fifth is done,
Here's "Merry Christmas
To everyone!"

2.